ROBERT SCHUMANN
SIXTEEN ALBUMLEAVES

Edited by Howard Ferguson

Introduction	*page* 2

5 ALBUMBLÄTTER – 5 ALBUMLEAVES: from *Bunte Blätter*, Op.99

1	Ziemlich langsam	3
2	Schnell	4
3	Ziemlich langsam	6
4	Sehr langsam	7
5	Langsam	8

11 PIECES: from *Albumblätter*, Op.124

6	Leides Ahnung – Foreboding of Sorrow (2)	9
7	Walzer – Waltz (4)	10
8	Elfe – Elf (17)	11
9	Phantasietanz – Fantastic Dance (5)	12
10	Ländler – Ländler (7)	13
11	Wiegenliedchen – Cradle Song (6)	14
12	Larghetto – Larghetto (13)	15
13	Leid ohne Ende – Unending Sorrow (8)	16
14	Walzer – Waltz (15)	18
15	Phantasiestück – Fantastic Piece (19)	19
16	Schlummerlied – Lullaby (16)	22

The original numbering of the pieces is shown within brackets

THE ASSOCIATED BOARD OF
THE ROYAL SCHOOLS OF MUSIC

INTRODUCTION

ROBERT SCHUMANN (1810-1856)

In spite of their late opus-numbers, most of the pieces in this volume were written before Schumann was 30 – that is to say, concurrently with many of his greatest piano works and shortly before the wonderful outpouring of songs that celebrated his engagement to Clara Wieck.

As a rule Schumann used German tempo indications, sometimes supplementing them with metronome marks. In the present edition the more familiar Italian equivalents of the former have been added within square brackets by the editor. As there were no metronome marks in the original edition of either *Bunte Blätter* or *Albumblätter*, the editor has added a suggested tempo at the end of each piece. It should be understood, however, that these editorial markings are neither authoritative nor binding.

Schumann's pedal indications often consist of no more than the words *Mit Pedal*, or simply *Pedal*, at the beginning of a movement, implying that the player should use whatever pedal is required. In this connection it is helpful to remember two points: (1) the presence of rests and/or staccatos does not necessarily preclude the use of pedal; and (2) it is always needed to sustain the low note(s) of a chord or arpeggio that cannot be stretched by the hand.

The present texts are taken from the 1st editions: *Bunte Blätter: 14 Stücke für das Pianoforte . . . Op.99*; F.W. Arnold, Elberfeld [1852], Pl.Nos.331-8, and *Albumblätter: 20 Clavierstücke . . . Op.124*; F.W. Arnold, Elberfeld [1854], Pl.Nos.355-8. These, rather than the autographs, represent Schumann's definitive thoughts.

Thanks are due to the British Library Board for providing access to the 1st editions, and for allowing them to be used in preparing the present texts.

HOWARD FERGUSON
Cambridge 1985

5 Albumblätter — 5 Albumleaves

from *Bunte Blätter*, Op.99

Ziemlich langsam [Lento ma non troppo]

SCHUMANN
1841

Ed: ♩ = c.56

‡ Brahms used this piece as the theme of his *Variations on a theme by Robert Schumann*, Op.9. His ninth Variation is based on the second piece.

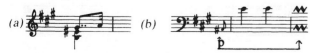

4

Schnell [Moderato]

1838

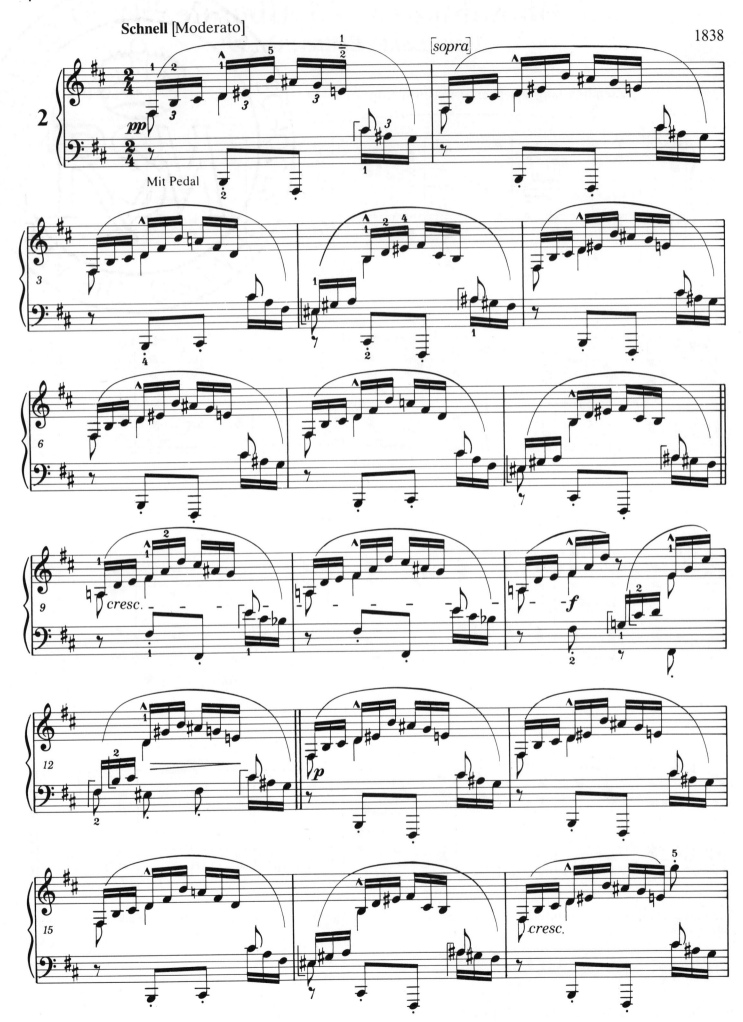

Ed: ♩ = c.76

Ziemlich langsam, sehr gesangvoll [Andantino cantabile]

Mit Pedal

Ed: ♩ = c.120

(a) In order to avoid harmonic confusion, the gracenotes should here probably coincide with the beat,

thus: , etc.

AB 1935

Sehr langsam [Lento]

Ed: ♪ = c.66

1) B.6, l.h. lower line, note 5: the source has C(flat); but A(flat) is more probable.

8

Ed: ♪ = c.76
(a) Gracenotes before the beat. (b)

11 Pieces
from *Albumblätter*, Op.124

Leides Ahnung
Foreboding of Sorrow

1835

Ed: ♩ = c.60

† Originally the fifth of nine Studies, or Variations, on the opening theme of the slow movement of Beethoven's 7th Symphony.
(1st edition: Schumann, *Exercises [Beethoven-Etüden]*, ed. Robert Münster; Henle, 1976.)

AB 1935

Walzer
Waltz

1835

Ed: ♩. = c.58
(a) Gracenotes before the beat.

Elfe
Elf

So schnell als möglich [Prestissimo]

1835

Ed: ♩ = c.72

Phantasietanz
Fantastic Dance

Sehr rasch [Vivace molto]

Ed: ♩ = c.84

Ländler †
Ländler

Sehr mäßig [Moderato molto]

1836

(a) The r.h. arpeggios begin and end simultaneously with those of the l.h.

Ed: ♩ = c.132

† A Ländler is a slow German waltz.
(a) The r.h. arpeggios begin and end simultaneously with those of the l.h.
(b) Players with small hands may prefer in bb.8-15 to take the top l.h. note with the r.h. thumb.
(c) Gracenotes before the beat.

Wiegenliedchen
Cradle Song

im Tempo [a tempo]

dimin.

Larghetto
Larghetto

1832

12

Ed: ♩ = c.100

Ed: ♩. = c.50

(a) For small hands: r.h. (Depress the diamond-shaped note silently.)

AB 1935

Leid ohne Ende
Unending Sorrow

(a) In bb.1-3 the italic fingering is Schumann's; but players may prefer the editorial alternative shown. R.h. b.10 proves that the gracenotes come before the beat. The pedal is changed on the lowest note of each pair, in spite of the slight harmonic haze that this produces.

1) B.16, l.h. gracenote 2: the source has $\frac{B}{G}$(flat): but see the more probable b.45.

Erstes Tempo [Tempo primo]

Ed: ♩ = c.72, b.22 ♩ = c.96

(b)

Walzer
Waltz

1832

Mit Pedal

Ed: ♩ = c.108

Phantasiestück
Fantastic Piece

Leicht, etwas graziös [Leggiero e grazioso]

1839

im Tempo [a tempo]

ritard.

Ed: ♪ = c.100

[sopra   sotto]

(a) Gracenotes before the beat.

AB 1935

Schlummerlied
Lullaby

1841

Mit Pedal

(a) Gracenotes before the beat.

[*sotto*]

1) B.3, 1.h. note 3: the source has C; but in the D.C., which the source printed in full, it is the more probable E(flat).

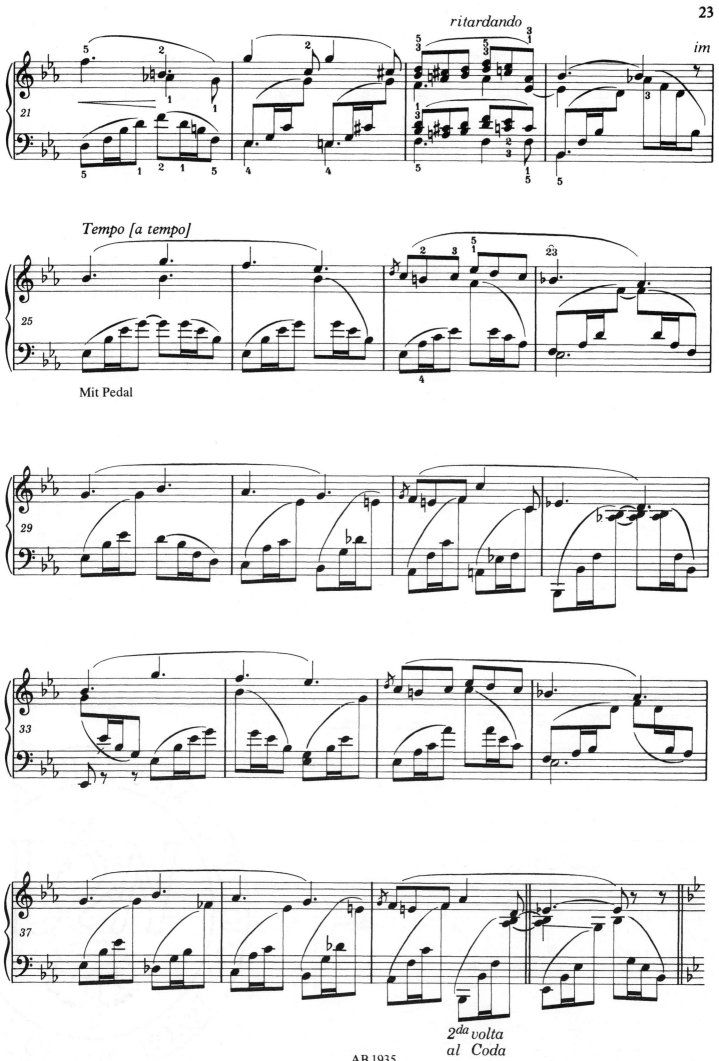

Ed: ♩. = c.60, b.41. ♩.=c.52

Reproduced and printed by
Halstan & Co. Ltd., Amersham, Bucks., England

6/06